MW00379554

Flavia

Our memories,

like our dreams,
are ours alone and tell our story.

This is a tale of
the heart and soul.

_____
(name)

_____
(beginning date)

ISBN 0-7683-2046-1

Text by Flavia and Lisa Weedn

Illustrations by Flavia Weedn

© Weedn Family Trust

www.flavia.com

All rights reserved.

Published in 1998 by Cedco Publishing Company.

100 Pelican Way, San Rafael, California 94901

For a free catalog of other Cedco® products, please write

to the address above, or visit our website: www.cedco.com

Printed in Hong Kong

3 5 7 9 10 8 6 4 2

No part of this book may be reproduced

in any manner whatsoever without written permission

except in the case of reprints in the context of reviews.

The artwork for each picture is digitally mastered using acrylic on canvas.

A PERSONAL TALE OF LOVE AND ROMANCE

Heart and Soul

Flavia and Lisa Weedn

Illustrated by Flavia Weedn

Cedco Publishing Company • San Rafael, California

Love is everything.

It is the sharing of songs and
of silences, and the holding of memories only the heart can see. It is the
flame from which we light the torch of life, a kind of nourishmer
we embrace in the quiet of our souls.

Love exists in many forms and its touch shapes us
into the people we become. In its infinite layers,
love is the very strength upon which
we live and breathe, hope and dream.
When we pause to reflect upon the many
chapters of our lives, we find that our most
cherished memories are born of
the heart - be it the love we learned from our parents or
the love we give our children, the lessons learned through
heartache or the magical encounter of a
soul mate.

Whether we're dreaming of love,

newly in love, or deeply committed,

the telling of our story becomes an important piece to our living.

For in the telling, we discover radiant truths

about who we are, and all that we are destined to be.

This journal is meant to become your story,

a uniquely personal tale of how love and romance,

passion and desire have enriched your life.

May you fill each page with the wonder

of your memories, your hopes for tomorrow,

and all the glory found in the sharing

of life's finest gift,

Love.

Its music may be different to each of us,

but oh, how beautiful the dance.

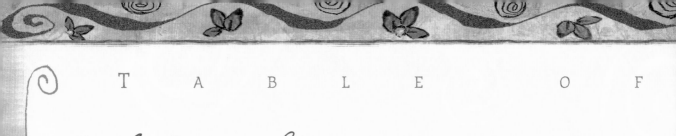

CONTENTS

At Long Last Love

Honoring Love's Dream

The Legacy of Love

Close to my heart is the TIME

of beginning, for this was the time

when all my dreams were born. In my earliest youth

I recognized LOVE, was drawn

to it by my very nature,

for CARE was,

and still is,

the language of

MY SOUL.

Reflections

of

Love

The Beginning

What I learned about love from my parents

Others who taught me the meaning of love

Love's Teachings

Legacies to keep

Legacies to put away

The Seed of Dreams

Pieces of my childhood

A Garden of Memories

Cherished times

If

while you

are a child,

just one

someone loves

you uncritically,

then you will

have love

to give for

the rest of

your life.

Treasures Untold

A letter to my parents

Dream Makers

A letter to the dream makers of my youth

The words

we most want

to say are

difficult to find

sometimes.

Their journey

begins far,

far away,

somewhere

in the heart.

First Flutterings

The first time I fell in love

Who I shared my secrets with

Of the Heart

Names and faces I recall

_____
_____
_____
_____
_____
_____
_____
_____

Memorable places and events

_____
_____
_____
_____
_____
_____
_____
_____

Sacred Gifts

Tender gifts my heart received

Love's Awakenings

Lessons learned through heartache

Just to

have felt

love's spark

was glory

enough.

To My First Love

The words I wish I would have said

In Gratitude

What I would say to you now

You

were

my

innocence,

and in

your eyes

I recognized

the beauty

of all

that

could be.

It is important to my HEART to shed my armor, to remove my mask and to let the RADIANCE of my inner self shine through. Only then do I recognize the AUTHENTICITY of me; only then can I let my spirit dance freely enough to behold the depth of BEAUTY my eyes can rarely see.

Discovering

Myself

The Looking Glass

Who I see when I look in the mirror

_____

_____

_____

_____

_____

_____

_____

_____

Who I hope to become

_____

_____

_____

_____

_____

_____

_____

_____

_____

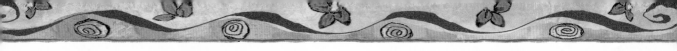

A Closer View

My favorite aspects of who I am

_____

_____

_____

_____

_____

_____

_____

_____

_____

My least favorite pieces of me

_____

_____

_____

_____

_____

_____

_____

_____

_____

Private Conversations

My questions, doubts, and fears about love

With Myself

What I need to let go of and where I hope to grow

Take

the risk

and be

unafraid

to love,

for nothing

is as

necessary

to the

heart.

Becoming More

The kind of partner I hope to be

The Art of Longing

The partner I've always dreamt of

Love

begins

with

a

dream.

A Love Affair

Poetry that speaks my heart

Art that moves me

Words and Music

Lyrics that inspire me

Books I love

Sacred Truths

My passions

Impassioned Soul

My beliefs

By recognizing the strength of our convictions and the beauty of our faith, we discover the treasures we have to share.

Learning to Love

A letter to my heart

The Dream

Personal goals and promises

Learning

to love

ourselves

is the

foundation

for all

other

loves.

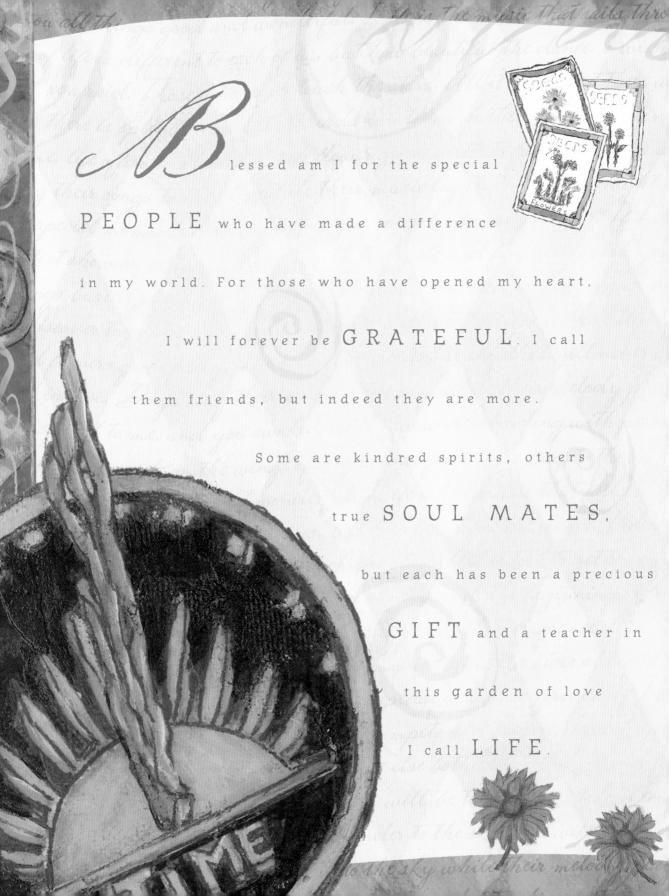

*B*lessed am I for the special

PEOPLE who have made a difference

in my world. For those who have opened my heart,

I will forever be GRATEFUL. I call

them friends, but indeed they are more.

Some are kindred spirits, others

true SOUL MATES,

but each has been a precious

GIFT and a teacher in

this garden of love

I call LIFE.

Nothing
by
Chance

Meeting Friends

Special people who have crossed my path

Along the Way

How they enlightened me

Some

people

come into

our lives and

quickly go.

Some stay

for a while,

leave footprints

on our hearts,

and we are

never, ever

the same.

Discoveries

Memories of dating

_____

_____

_____

_____

_____

_____

_____

_____

The players involved

_____

_____

_____

_____

_____

_____

_____

_____

_____

Laughter and Tears

Awkward and humorous moments

Stories to tell

Then Came You

Discovering a best friend and soul mate

How we met

Bright Spirit

Parallels in our lives

Shared truths and passions

Golden Threads

Images of times shared

Life's Tapestry

Memories to cherish

That we

could live

our lives

at the

same time

on earth,

how

incredible

God's plan.

True Friend

If not for you, I might have never known

The many things you taught me

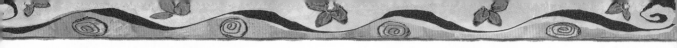

Kindred Heart

What I learned about myself through your eyes

_____

_____

_____

_____

_____

_____

_____

_____

_____

_____

_____

_____

What I learned about love

_____

_____

_____

_____

_____

_____

_____

_____

_____

_____

_____

Forever

Words of gratitude and praise

Thankful

What I wish I could say to you now

If I

could sit

across

the porch

from God,

I'd thank Him

for lending

me you.

And in that instant, something inside of me knew. It wasn't the tinkling of a bell, not bright lights or even fireworks. It was LOVE'S calm and WONDROUS moment of complete recognition. My SOUL had finally found its way HOME.

At

Long Last

Love

Sweet Beginnings

How we met and the story we tell

Private Thoughts

What we first thought of each other

Within

the

mystery

of life,

we met.

It was

written

in the

stars.

Love's First Recognition

I knew it was love when

My favorite things about you

Two Souls, One Heart

The passions we share

Special moments I remember

Passion

Our first dance

Our first kiss

Desire

Our first night together

Our first morning after

Love's Dance

The way you make me feel

Inspirations

All that you inspire in me

When
two
hearts
meet,
oh, the
dances
dreams
can
make.

Souvenirs

My favorite phrases of yours

Soft whispers

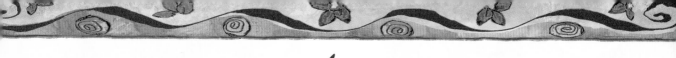

Of Affection

Lines from love letters

_____

Gifts and keepsakes

Memories to Keep

Memorable Dates

Parties and Celebrations

Hand in Hand

Vacations and Explorations

Discoveries

loved you before we ever met. You were

the HOPE that carried me, the vision that gave

me strength. And now, by some GREAT

MIRACLE, you are here. Blessed am

I for the touch of your hand, the depth

of your gaze, your

unspoken GIFT of

understanding. For this,

and so much more, I give

to you my HEART, all of my

promises, my FOREVER

and always.

Honoring Love's Dream

Forever and Always

Private moments and dreams

Committing

Personal vows

Love's

words

and

promises,

and

dreams

of

tomorrow.

Celebrations

Of the Heart

Life's

greatest

celebrations

are

anniversaries

of the

heart.

Looking Ahead

Hopes for tomorrow

Relationship Goals

Building the Dream

Personal aspirations

Professional goals

Safe and Warm

The place we call home

Where the Heart Is

Visions of what will be

Side

by side

we live

the dream,

and home

is wherever

we are.

Private Passions

Cherished Intimacy

Whispered Desires

Divine Secrets

Love

is the

passionate

dance

between

two

hearts.

Keeping Love New

Loving Our Togetherness

Celebrating Our Separateness

Overcoming Challenges

She Said, He Said

Finding Answers, Making Resolutions, and Letting Go

The HEART'S capacity for love

could fill the entire space between heaven and earth, and

the magnitude of its brilliance can only be measured by

the stars in the sky. Now that we have found true love,

let us share it with the world—and leave behind

a sprinkling of its STARDUST

so that others may

know and feel

and believe in the

MIRACLE.

The Legacy of Love

The Beauty

How love has changed my life

The Dance

Integrity and Virtues of Love

Sharing a

life together

is sharing

steps in time.

The music

is different

to each of us,

but how

beautiful

the dance.

Love By Example

The little things that matter

Truths Defined

The bigger things that matter

Life's greatest gift is to love and be loved in return. Love is all that matters.

Poetry

Of Love

Learn the
language
of the heart
and say
the words.
They may
mean more
than you
dare to
dream.

Songs

Of the Soul

Love

is the

sweet

music

of the

soul.

Wisdom of the Heart

Our letter to each other

Tomorrow's Dreams

Our list of dreams

When

they

said

all fairy

tales

must end,

they never

knew

about us.

A Gift of Love

The legacy we hope to offer future generations

Love

is the holding

of memories

only the heart

can see.

_____

(closing date)

Other Flavia Books for Adults:

Heaven and Earth
A Journal of Dreams and Awakenings

Dear Little One
A Memory Journal of Baby's First Year

Passages
A Woman's Personal Journey

Celebrations of Life
A Birthday and Anniversary Book

Kindred Spirits
An Illustrated Address Book

Flavia Books for Children:

The Little Snow Bear
The Enchanted Tree
The Elephant Prince
The Star Gift

Photo by Claudia Kunin

Flavia Weedn is one of America's leading contemporary inspirational writers and illustrators. Her work has touched the lives of millions for over three decades. Offering a kind of hope for the human spirit, Flavia portrays the basic excitement, simplicity and beauty she sees in the ordinary things of life. Lisa Weedn, Flavia's daughter and co-author, shares her mother's philosophy and passion. Their collaborative writings celebrate life and embrace meaningful core values. It is their wish to shine a beacon of hope into the lives of others by encouraging the belief that we all have a significant contribution to make in this lifetime and every dream can be realized. Their work includes numerous books, collections of fine stationery goods, giftware, and lifestyle products distributed worldwide. Flavia and Lisa live in Santa Barbara, California.

May your dreams ride on the wings of angels and find their way to the skies.
Wishing you all things good and wonderful. Life is the music that sails thro
The music of life is different to each of us, but how beautiful the dance. I wish
when you're afraid. Those who reach touch the stars. All it took to get there wa
true joy there is splendor, and its threads run through the beginning of eve
ges of time. life offers loveliness. Each flower gives birth to fragrance. then so
Days sing their songs to the sky while their music lights the stars at night.
May the special moments of today bring you special memories forever. If I co
the greatest show on earth—embrace it with trumpets and fanfare. I wish you
and things buried so deep so deep that no one else bothered to look for and fin
We will discover together, and our tomorrows will be the steps we take throug
here wild flowers grow freely. There is a wonder to the day that will never en
People fall in love. Days sing their songs to the sky while their melody plays
You are so special to me, and you bring understanding with passi
May your dreams ride on the wings of angels and find their way to the skies
Wishing you all things good and wonderful. Life is the music that sails thro
The music of life is different to each of us, but how beautiful the dance. I wish
when you're afraid. Those who reach touch the stars. All it took to get there wa
true joy there is splendor, and its threads run through the beginning of eve
ges of time. life offers loveliness. Each flower gives birth to fragrance. then so
Days sing their songs to the sky while their music lights the stars at night.
May the special moments of today bring you special memories forever. If I co
the greatest show on earth—embrace it with trumpets and fanfare. I wish you
and things buried so deep so deep that no one else bothered to look for and
We will discover together, and our tomorrows will be the steps we take
here wild flowers grow freely. There is a wonder to the day that
People fall in love.

your dreams ride on the wings of angels and find their way to the skies.
bring you all things good and wonderful. Life is the music that sails through
music of life is different to each of us, but how beautiful the dance. I wish you
when you're afraid. Those who reach touch the stars. All it took to get there was
true joy there is splendor, and its threads run through the beginning of every
of time, life offers loveliness. Each flower gives birth to fragrance, then softly
days sing their songs to the sky while their music lights the stars at night. All
the special moments of today bring you special memories forever. If I could
greatest show on earth—embrace it with trumpets and fanfare. I wish you a
things buried so deep so deep that no one else bothered to look for and find
together, and our tomorrows will be the steps we take through
grow freely. There is a wonder to the sky that will never
sing their songs to the sky while their melody plays